WORD PROCESSING & TYPING

Kate Fraser

Consultant: Jenny Collyer
Designed by Kim Blundell

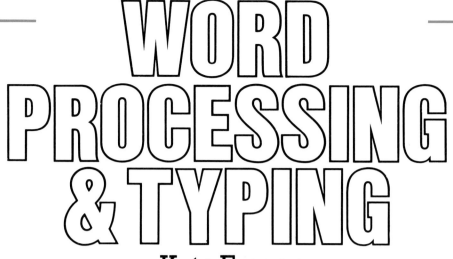

Dear ____
Thank you for the wonderful
____ you sent me for my
birthday. It is really
indescribable.
    I hope you are well and
that I will see you soon.
Love Kate

Birthday presents

Uncle Cecil · Book of Newts
Aunt Adie · Boxing gloves
Billy Fraser · Bagpipe case
Grandma · Socks
Cousin Joe · Sewing kit
Grandpa · Pickled herrings
Great Aunt Suzy · Roller skates
Sandy · Chewing gum
Brian · Nothing

Edited by Judy Tatchell

Illustrated by Brenda Haw, Chris Lyon
Kim Blundell, Martin Newton, Roger Stewart
and Adam Willis

WITH
TOUCH-TYPING
GUIDE

Contents

First published in 1985 by
Usborne Publishing Ltd, 20 Garrick Street,
London WC2E 9BJ, England.
Copyright © 1985 Usborne Publishing.
Printed in Belgium
The name Usborne and the device 🐝 are
Trade Marks of Usborne Publishing Ltd. All

About this book

This book is a guide to word processing and typing for absolute beginners. The first few pages tell you what a word processor is and describes the many things you can use one for.

Some machines are designed just to be word processors, but you can also buy word processing programs on disks, tapes, or chips to use with a home computer. You can find out more about the difference between these systems, and about the other equipment you need if you want to use a word processor, on pages 8-11.

Later in the book there is a section on how to touch type. Simple diagrams show you which fingers to use on which keys, and there are puzzles and games to help you speed up your typing.

Pages 16-35 explain how word processors work and show you how to use them. There are more games and puzzles to help you. You will have to check in your manual for detailed instructions on using your own word processor, as they all work in different ways.

The book contains advice on how to look after your own word processor. You can also read about how to prevent the physical effects that using a word processor for a long time may have on you, such as eye strain or backache.

Finally, if you decide you want to buy a word processor, there is lots of advice on how to choose one and information on current makes in a Buyer's Guide at the back of the book.

What is word processing?

Word processing is using a computer to help you write, store and print out words. A computer which is being used for word processing is called a word processor. It can save you lots of time and make many of the tasks you connect with writing easier and more fun. You can use it for many things, from writing letters to preparing complicated documents. Some of the other ways you can use word processors are shown on pages 6-7.

Screen

I am a word processor

Keyboard

When you use a word processor, you type on a keyboard and what you type appears on a screen. You can then alter your typing, for example correct mistakes or change words, before you tell the computer to print it out. This means that when you finally print out what you have typed, it is exactly how you want it. Some of the things you can do with word processors are shown on these two pages.

Printing out

You can print out what you have typed as many times as you want, without having to retype it, or use carbon paper or a photocopier each time.

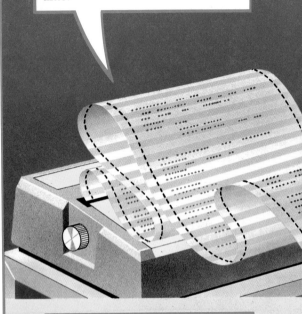

Storing what you write

You can store what you have typed by copying it on to special disks or tapes. You can find out more about these on pages 9 and 26.

Recalling what you have stored

It is easy to recall anything you have typed and stored on tape or disk, by transferring it back to the screen.

Saving space

You can store the equivalent of a file full of sheets of paper on one disk smaller than a single record, or on an ordinary cassette tape.

4

Merging

You can combine or merge information stored on a disk or cassette, such as names and addresses, with other information, such as letters or invitations, that you are currently typing on your keyboard.

Making pages

You can divide what you are writing into numbered pages, with centred headings.

Inserting new words

You can insert new words anywhere you like into text you have already typed. With some systems you can replace words on your screen by writing new words over them.

```
           Word Processing Sale

Dear.........

I am writing to enquiask
whether you would be
interested in buying
a word porcessor. *My uncle
Arbuthnot gave me a new wierd
prucessor for my birthday,
so I am selling my old
world proscissor second hand.*
I don't know how much I shall
ask for it. It depends who
offers the most. I am also
writing to the following
people:
      Bobby Byron
       Sally Shelley
        Lance Nesbit
         Chuck Chekhov
          Jamie Wordsworth
           Jill Shakespeare
t me know if you ar  interested?
         With best wis es,
              Julian
```

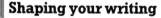

Removing words

When you make mistakes, or change your mind about what you have written, you can instantly remove (or delete) words or lines and the space they have taken up. This is much neater and quicker than crossing things out.

Marking sections

Using special markers, e.g. ★, you can pick out sections of your writing to move, delete, copy, store or print out separately from the rest.

New lines

When you reach the end of a line on the screen, most word processors automatically start a new one for you.

Shaping your writing

You can arrange what you have written on the screen to be the precise shape, length and width you want. This can be printed out exactly how you plan it. Pages 22-23 show you more about how to do this.

Replacing words

You can replace a word instantly with another word throughout a whole document, e.g. you could change "word processor" to "computer" all through this letter (provided you had corrected the spelling of word processor first).

What can you do with a word processor?

Word processors are used by many people for many different tasks. Some of these are shown here and you will probably come across several more. Lots of offices and organizations have replaced their typewriters with word processors. At home, people often find that one of the most useful things they can do with a home computer is to use it as a word processor.

What all word processing tasks have in common is that they make the job of writing and storing information easier.

At home

Here are some of the things you could use a word processor for at home.

Letters

You can use a word processor for one-off letters or for duplicating things like party invitations or thank you letters. You just insert a different name and address each time.

Records

> I propose . . .   Seconded . . .

If you belong to a group, club or committee, you can use a word processor to keep agendas and minutes of meetings.

You can keep accounts of housekeeping budgets, bills, savings or pocket money.

Personal memory

You can store Christmas card lists, birthdays, telephone numbers, menus, train timetables etc.

Diary

A diary planner for the whole family can be kept in one place, with holiday dates, outings, social events, appointments etc.

Creative writing

Lots of authors use word processors when writing books. You could also use a word processor to write short stories, articles or essays.

In offices

Word processors are used in lots of offices to speed up typing jobs and make them less repetitive.

Writing documents

Complicated documents can be put together, altered, and copies made of them.

Identical letters, each addressed to a different person, can be mass produced.

Spelling check

Some word processors can store a dictionary of up to 150,000 words. They check the spelling of each word you type and highlight mistakes.

Laying out text

A word processor makes laying out, or designing, forms, documents and letters much easier.

Storing files

I never knew filing cabinets came that small!

Many offices use word processor disks instead of filing cabinets to store letters and documents.

Other uses

Instantly, sir.

Can you get each Trogladite a copy of his part?

Film and theatre producers use word processors to extract different parts from lengthy scripts to give to different actors.

Schools

Word processing is taught in many schools and colleges to give pupils a skill which might help them find a job when they leave. It is also used to help with spelling and creative writing. Some children find that using a word processor and seeing what they write printed out makes writing easier and more exciting.

Electronic mail

You can use some word processors to send messages to others by connecting them to the telephone system. Information is sent in the form of electronic signals. This is quicker than posting letters. It is cheaper than a phone call because information is sent very fast and there is no chatting on the phone.

Different kinds of word processor

There are two main kinds of word processor. A computer which is specially designed for the job is called a dedicated word processor. You can also use an ordinary computer such as a home computer as a word processor. It needs a word processing program and you also need a disk drive or cassette recorder and a printer.

A dedicated word processor has a good quality screen designed to cut down on eye strain. This screen can be tilted to suit you.

The keyboard is hard-wearing. You can adjust its height and angle.

Dedicated word processors ▶

A dedicated word processor has a built-in word processing program. The program (called software) and the parts of the word processor (called hardware) are designed to help busy typists to work fast and accurately.

Dedicated function keys

A dedicated word processor has keys on it labelled with instructions such as those in the picture on the right. These are called function keys or command keys. They refer to things you can do when working on your text. You can find out more about this later in the book.

Dedicated function keys

Separate or shared systems

Some word processors share printers, disk drives or both. These are called shared resource systems. Each person has a keyboard and screen, but typing is stored and printed out on the shared equipment.
This type of system is often used in large organizations as it can be more economical.

Some word processors have their own printer and disk drive and so are completely self-contained. They are used by one person only and are called stand-alone systems.

Shared disk drive

Word processor

Shared printers may be kept in a separate room where the noise does not distract anyone.

◀ Computers with word processing software

You can buy word processing programs for ordinary, programmable computers. When you have loaded the program you can use the computer like a dedicated word processor. Although they do not have dedicated function keys with commands printed on them, many computers have numbered function keys like those below. The program gives each of these a particular job so that they behave like dedicated function keys.

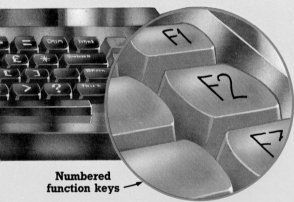

Numbered function keys ──

Which word processor?

Here are some of the advantages and disadvantages of using either a dedicated word processor or word processing software on a programmable computer.

 Dedicated word processors are usually more efficient because they are specially designed for the job.

 You cannot use a dedicated word processor for any other computing jobs and they are usually expensive.

 You can buy quite a cheap computer and still use it for word processing. As better software is developed, you can replace your word processing program with a better one.

Software: tape, disk or chip?

Word processing software may come on tape, disk or chip. What you buy depends on what is available for your computer and what you can afford. There is a Buyer's Guide listing some of the different makes of software available on pages 38-41.

Cassette tape

This is the cheapest form of software. You need a cassette recorder to use it. It takes much longer to load the program into the computer and store your text than if you use a program on disk.

Disk

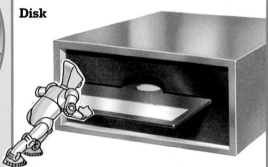

A program on disk loads into the computer very fast and storing your text only takes a few seconds. It costs more than a taped program and you need a disk drive to use it.

Chip

Software on chip costs about the same as disk software. The chip comes installed inside the computer or in a slot-in cartridge. When you want to use the program, you type an instruction on the keyboard. You store text on either cassette tape or disk.

Other equipment you need

If you want to use a home computer for word processing, you will probably have to buy some extra equipment. You need a disk drive or a cassette recorder to store what you have typed. Otherwise, every time you switch your computer off you lose everything you have written. You also need a printer to print out what you have typed on to paper. What you buy depends on what you can afford and what works with your computer.

Cassette recorders

You can use an ordinary cassette recorder to store what you type on your word processor. You give each batch of typing (called a file) a title, or filename, before you store it.

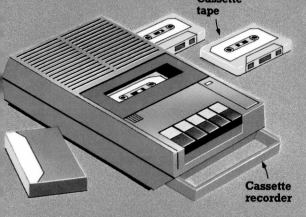

Cassette tape

Cassette recorder

A cassette recorder is quite cheap but it works slowly. Also, when you want to transfer a file back into your computer, it has to wind through the cassette tape looking for the file, which can take time.

Most home computers have a socket for connecting a cassette recorder. If you do not have a lead with the correct plugs at each end, you can get one made up by a dealer.

Saving and loading

Storing files or programs on tape or disk is known as saving them. Transferring files or programs from tape or disk back to your computer is called loading them.

Disk drives

Before you buy a disk drive, check with the dealer that it will work with your computer.

Disk

Disk drive

Slot for disk.

A disk drive does the same job as a cassette recorder, but stores files on a disk instead of a cassette tape. It can save and load files for you in a few seconds. A disk drive is about ten times as expensive as a cassette recorder.

Using a disk drive

To computer   Disk interface   To disk drive
allows information to pass between disk drive and computer.

Before your computer can work with a disk drive, it needs some extra circuitry called a disk interface. This allows information to pass between the computer and disk drive. Check in your manual whether your computer already has an interface built in. If not, you can get one fitted by a dealer.

You also need a disk operating system (DOS) which tells your computer how to use the disk drive. A DOS is usually supplied on a disk with your disk drive, or on a chip fitted inside your computer.

Types of printer*

Dot matrix printers

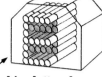

Pins making letter shape.

Dot matrix print head.

Some dot matrix printers are quite cheap. The outline of each letter is pushed out from a block of pins called the dot matrix print head. The higher the number of pins, the finer the quality of letter. The cheaper ones print about 80 characters per second (c.p.s.) and the more expensive ones up to about 350 c.p.s.

Thermal printers

These are a type of dot matrix printer. They work by burning the dots which make up letter shapes on to special, coated paper. They are very cheap, quiet, reliable machines, but they produce rough-looking characters which are difficult to read.

Daisy wheel, thimble and golfball printers

Golfball print head.

Thimble print head.

Daisy wheel print head.

These printers have a "print head" which has all the letters, numbers and punctuation marks moulded on to it. This may be in the shape of a wheel, a thimble, or a golfball. The print head rotates and the letter is pressed against an ink ribbon on to the paper. They are generally slower than dot matrix printers, printing between 20-55 characters per second, but they give much better quality printing.

Other kinds of printer

The two other main kinds of printer are ink jet and laser beam printers. These print very fast, but are very expensive.

For more about printers, see pages 28-29.

Paper feeding

Some printers use continuous sheets of paper with holes down the side. The paper is perforated so you can tear it up into separate sheets. The printer pulls the paper through it on evenly spaced pins. This is called pin or tractor feeding.

Other printers let you feed single sheets of paper such as headed notepaper through them. This is called friction feeding. Some printers can use either pin or friction feeding.

Pin feed printer

Perforated edges

Different type styles

This is condensed

This is bold

Most dot matrix printers can print different type styles, including bold, condensed and extended characters. You can change the print head on daisy wheel, golfball and thimble printers to get many different styles and different size lettering.

Acoustic hoods

Many printers make an irritating grating noise when printing. You can reduce this by half by putting a transparent cover called an acoustic hood over the printer.

11

How to touch type

Touch typing means typing without looking at the keys. This allows you to look at the screen or paper you are typing on to check for mistakes. When you get good at it, you will be able to copy things very fast, as you can read the material you are copying while you type.

Touch typing takes a lot of practice. The main thing is to get used to using the correct finger on each key. These pages show you which finger to use on each key, and there are some practice exercises at the bottom.

Which finger, which key?

Most typewriter and computer keyboards are laid out like the picture on the opposite page. Computers also have extra keys with other functions which you can read about on page 17.

You can see which finger to use for each key by looking at the colour of the key in the keyboard picture and at the picture below. All the yellow keys, for instance, are pressed by your middle fingers. The keyboard picture is divided into two halves, to show you whether to use your right or left hand.

Guide key letters

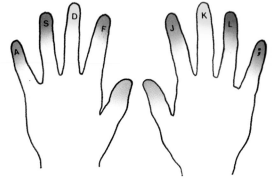

The letters shown on the fingers above are on eight keys called the guide keys. You rest your fingers on these when you start typing, and return each finger to its guide key after pressing a different key.

The shift key   A ⇨ a   SHIFT ⇨ A

Normally, when you press a letter key you get a small, or "lower case" letter. If you press a letter key while holding down the shift key you get a capital, or "upper case" letter. Pressing a key which has two symbols on it with the shift key, gives you the top character shown on that key. Use the little finger of the hand opposite the one in use to hold down the shift key.

Shift lock

Pressing this locks the shift key down. All the letters you type are capitals until you release the shift lock by pressing it again.

The space bar

This makes a space between each word. You hit it with either thumb.

Practising touch-typing

When you first practise a word or a phrase, glance down to check where the letters are. Then try typing it again without looking at your keyboard. When you can type it without looking and without making a mistake, move on to the next word or phrase. Always remember to return your fingers to the guide keys after hitting each key.

Typing speed

Don't worry too much about speed to begin with – it will improve as you get to know your keyboard. Just concentrate on using the right finger for each key.

Left-hand side — Space bar — Right-hand side

Number and punctuation keys

Keys which you use less often than letter keys, such as number and some punctuation keys, are too far from your guide keys to touch type, so when you strike them you glance down. You generally strike a number key with the finger from the guide key below it. Use your little finger for the nearest punctuation keys. For keys further away, use whichever finger feels most comfortable.

Starting a new line

Carriage return lever

Manual typewriters have a lever you pull to start a new line of type. On electric typewriters you press a key called RETURN to do this. Word processors start a new line of type automatically. You can also make them do this, to start a new paragraph, for instance, by pressing RETURN.

Guide key practice

Place your fingers on the guide keys. Now try typing out the following words which use the guide keys. Use your thumb for the space bar.

ass add fad all lass falls lads dad alas ask salad

a lass has salad;
a lad had a glass;

a lad shall fall;
a glad lass has a fall;

Now try typing out the phrases in the speech bubbles.

Touch-typing questionnaire

When you feel confident about where the guide keys are, you can start getting used to touch-typing other keys by answering this questionnaire. Try typing the answer to each question without looking at the keys.

1) Name?
2) Address?
3) Date of birth?
4) Height?
5) Weight?
6) Hair colour?
7) Colour of eyes?
8) Favourite food?
9) Favourite drink?
10) Favourite T.V. programme?
11) Hobby?
12) Ambition?

When you can touch-type the answers to these questions, try some of the more difficult exercises over the page.

13

Practising touch typing

If you practise the following exercises carefully your typing will improve and you will find it easier to do. If you are using a typewriter, you will need lots of rough paper. Get practice by typing everything you can, as well as these exercises, including letters to friends, lists and messages.

Things to remember

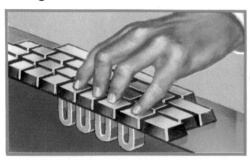

1. Think of the guide keys as magnets, pulling your fingers back to them.
2. To remind yourself where each key is, and which finger to use, look at the keyboard diagram on the previous page and not at your hands.
3. Only glance at the keyboard when you have to strike a number or punctuation key.

Rhymes

Fox box socks locks clocks knocks

Type out these six rhyming words. Then see if you can type out five rhymes for each of the words below.

Ring, table, tan, whale, mate, rain, sent, tank, scary, plum, rumble.

Carriage return

Type out the lines on the right, using your carriage return lever or RETURN key to start each new line.

Alphabet sentences

The quick brown fox jumps over the lazy dog.
Six squirrels were keenly jumping as the badger from the nearby zoo came into view.

These sentences contain all the letters of the alphabet. See if you can type them out without any mistakes.

Lists
Type out the following:

1. The names of all your friends.
2. Everything you ate yesterday.
3. The days of the week.
4. The months of the year.
5. Your least favourite television programmes.
6. Your favourite pop groups.
7. All the flavours of ice cream you can think of.
8. All the colours in the rainbow.
9. The furniture in the room you are sitting in.
10. All the places you have been on holiday.
11. All the clothes you are wearing at the moment.

Alphabet

Without looking at the keyboard, try typing out the alphabet from a to z. Do it first with a space between each letter, then in capital letters.

Punctuation

Type these sentences, putting in punctuation marks.

1. What an extraordinary person he said
2. Do you really like artichokes Henry
3. Those nuts the ones I ate yesterday had very hard shells

The
The longest
The longest word
The longest word in
The longest word in qwertyuiop
The longest word in qwertyuiop is
The longest word in qwertyuiop is typewriter

Here is a story to type. Begin at the box labelled START. Touch type the sentences in it and then follow the typewriter ribbon to the next box and type that. Correct any typing errors as you go along.

At dawn he heard a loud noise next to the prison. He looked down and saw a huge machine outside.

START

A lonely letter was imprisoned in a brain cell, serving a life sentence. The prison was grim, and crawling with thoughts and ideas.

He saw with horror that he was being crushed against a dark, inky ribbon. Then everything went black.

Suddenly he felt himself being sucked through the bars on the window, flying through the air and into the huge clanking machine.

One day a new thought came to him.
   "Do you realize you could escape from this prison, and be free?" it asked.

That night the thought silently dropped something through the bars of the letter's cell. The letter found a scrap of paper with COHUT PIGNTY* scribbled on it.

When he woke up, he found himself surrounded by rows of other letters. They were all lying on a smooth white bed that seemed to stretch as far as he could see. He realized he would never be lonely again.

END

*The solution to these coded words is on page 44.

Starting word processing

Before you can start word processing you need to load a word processing program. A dedicated word processor will be supplied with its own program on a disk called a system disk. On the right are some of the things you may see displayed on the screen when you have loaded the program.

You can also find out about other things you may have to deal with before you can start using the word processor.

Passwords

If you are using a shared resource word processor (one which shares a printer and disk drives – see page 8) you usually need to type in a code, or password, before you start. Each person has a different password so the central computer which handles the storage and printing can keep material typed by different people separate.

Working disk

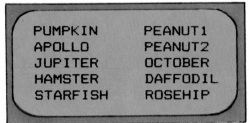

On some word processors you have to put a disk called the working disk into your disk drive before you can start typing. When you start it up, your word processor might show you a list, or directory, of files already stored on the working disk.* The directory might look like the one on the screen above.

16

Different screens

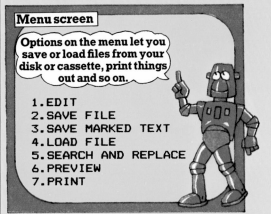

To start with, some word processors give you a list of options such as the one above. This is called a menu. You choose an option by typing the number beside it. To type text into your computer, you press the editing option. The computer wipes the menu off the screen and gives you a clear screen to work on, called the document screen.

ESCAPE key

On many computers you press a key to switch between the menu or command screen and the document screen. This key is usually called ESCAPE or EXIT.

Status line

`FILE:RAINBOW:LINE 50:PRINTING`

There is usually a line at the top or bottom of your screen showing the name of the file you are working on, instructions you give the computer, etc. This is called the status line.

Format line

Some word processors reserve a line at the top or bottom of the screen for your instructions about line lengths, margin positions, etc. This is called the format line. You can find out more about formatting on pages 22-23.

*You can find out about storing your text on pages 26-27.

Command screen

You type commands to save or load files, print things out and so on.

WORDSHIFT 4
EDITING: JINGLES

SAVE JINGLES

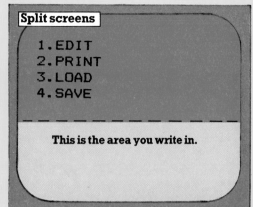

Split screens

1. EDIT
2. PRINT
3. LOAD
4. SAVE

This is the area you write in.

Some word processors do not have menus. Instead you type out instructions letter by letter or press function keys. The screen you type instructions on is called a command screen. To get the document screen, you either press the ESCAPE key (see below) or type an instruction which gives you a clear screen to work on.

Some screens may be divided up into different areas. For instance, there might be a section for a menu or commands, and a section for your typing. You can see both sections at once. Some split screens also display a help section which explains which keys you press to make your computer do different things.

Giving your computer instructions

Here are some of the ways you can give different word processors instructions.

Function keys

COPY — copies a marked section of text.*

DELETE — removes, or deletes text.

MOVE — moves a marked section of text.*

Function keys are keys on your keyboard which have specific jobs. On dedicated word processors they have instructions printed on them. Some common ones are described above.

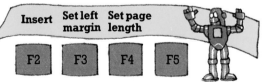

Insert	Set left margin	Set page length	
F2	F3	F4	F5

Function keys on a home computer do not have instructions printed on them. Instead, you may get a strip of paper with the program which you can place next to the keys. This tells you what each one does.

RETURN key

After you have typed out an instruction, or given the word processor information such as the name of a file, you need to press the RETURN or ENTER key. On a dedicated word processor this key may also be called EXECUTE, DO, ACTION or EFFECT. You do not need to press this key after using a function key or choosing an option from the menu.

Control key

CTRL + D = Delete character

CTRL + C = Centre the text

When you press this key down with certain other letters or numbers, it forms specific commands, called control codes. It may be labelled CTRL or CODE.

17

*You can find out how to mark sections of text on page 19.

Using your word processor

When you start using a word processor, you will find that one of the main advantages it has over a typewriter is that you can correct mistakes, alter words, or move chunks of text before you print anything out. These two pages show you the sort of thing you can do. Over the page are some games and exercises to help you practise them. Pages 22-23 show you how to arrange, or format, your text by altering line lengths, positions of margins and so on, so it can be printed out exactly how you want it.

The cursor

Your cursor may look like one of these.

The cursor is a little symbol on your screen which shows you where the next letter you type will appear. It moves along the line automatically as you type. You can also move the cursor round the screen using four keys, called cursor control keys. Each of these takes the cursor in a different direction, indicated by arrows on the keys. Some cursors flash on and off.

Removing text

Here are some of the ways you can remove, or delete, text on word processors.

Letters

Letter being deleted

Cursor

You can delete the last letter you typed by pressing the DELETE key. If you keep this pressed down it pushes the cursor backwards, deleting letters, until you release it.

Words and lines

You can delete words or lines of text by using a function key or control code (the control key plus another key). Your manual will tell you exactly how to do this.

Blocks of words

On some word processors, you can delete to a specific point in the text. You usually use a function key called DELETE TO, or a control code, with the word or letter you want to delete up to.

You can delete larger amounts by using special markers – see the "Using markers" section below.

Using markers

On many word processors you can instantly move around, delete or copy large blocks of text, by using special markers.

To set your markers, you move the cursor to the beginning of the block of text, using the cursor control keys. Press the function key, control code, or typed command to set the first marker. Then move the cursor to the end of the block, and press the same keys to set the second marker. On some computers you set markers by positioning your cursor and pressing RETURN.

Deleting

```
My uncle was a cheerful man,
who liked watching television
and playing billiards. *He was
a jolly person and a dedicated
billiards player and TV
watcher. When he wasn't
watching TV he was cheerfully
playing billiards.* I was very
fond of him.
```

Marker

To delete a block of text, you set your markers round it and then instruct your computer to delete it. There is usually a function key which you press to delete marked blocks of text.

Inserting and overwriting

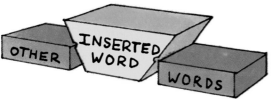

Word processors let you type in new words anywhere in your text. You can either add new words to what is already there (inserting), or replace what is already there by typing over it (overwriting). Some word processors let you do both. You usually press a function key to tell it which you want to do.

Realigning

When you delete words, the words that follow move back to close up the gap. If you insert words, the words that follow readjust to make room. This is called realigning. Sometimes you have to tell the word processor to realign your text – usually by pressing a function key.

Moving with markers

To move a marked chunk of text, position the cursor to where you want the block to go. You then press the function key, or the keys which tell your computer to move it.

> **Some machines give you a warning signal if you try to delete a large block.**

Copying

In the same way as moving text you can also copy blocks of text using markers. When you do this, the block you have marked stays where it is, but you can move a copy of it anywhere else in your text.

Search and replace

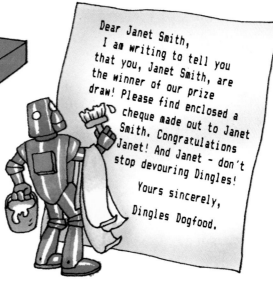

Dear Janet Smith,
I am writing to tell you that you, Janet Smith, are the winner of our prize draw! Please find enclosed a cheque made out to Janet Smith. Congratulations Janet! And Janet - don't stop devouring Dingles!
Yours sincerely,
Dingles Dogfood.

On many systems you can tell your computer to go through the whole text replacing one word with another. For instance, you can correct something spelt wrongly throughout a whole document, or replace one name with another, without having to go through it line by line.

You can save time by shortening long words which occur frequently by typing in just one or two letters. When you have finished, you can tell your computer to replace them with the real word.

Merging

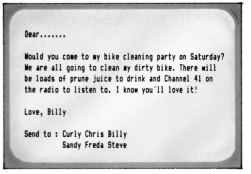

Dear.......

Would you come to my bike cleaning party on Saturday? We are all going to clean my dirty bike. There will be loads of prune juice to drink and Channel 41 on the radio to listen to. I know you'll love it!

Love, Billy

Send to : Curly Chris Billy
          Sandy Freda Steve

Some word processors let you join together, or merge, information stored on one tape or disk with information stored on another. If you have a lot of identical letters to write, you can merge a standard letter on one disk with a list of names and addresses on another. This is usually called mailmerge.

Practising word processing

The more you practise using your word processor, the easier it will become. Here are some games and exercises to help you use the keys and codes you have read about on the previous pages. On this page, you can practise deleting and inserting, and searching and replacing text. On the opposite page, you can find the answer to "Whodunnit?" by using your markers to move and delete text.

Suzy's sister

Suzy's sister sent Suzy's sister's Siamese spider seven sacks of Suzy's sister's semolina. When Suzy's sister's Siamese spider sampled Suzy's sister's seven sacks of semolina, Suzy's sister's spider sang.

Ambitions

I want to be a fishmonger when I grow up.

Type out this sentence. Then delete "I want" and "I grow", and replace with names of friends and relatives, e.g. John wants, my sister wants. Now delete "fishmonger" and replace it with other jobs, e.g. trapeze artist, polar explorer, lumberjack and so on.

When you have typed out the above sentences, replace the words Suzy's, sister, sister's, spider and semolina with other words beginning with the same letter, e.g. Barny's brother, budgie and beetroot. If you have a search and replace key or code on your word processor, use this to seek out and replace words. Otherwise, just delete and insert them.

Steps

Type out this sentence:
Who was the first man to walk on the moon?

Now carry out the instructions below and the answer will appear on your screen.

Insert "strong" before man.

Insert "charming" after "strong". Delete "to walk".

Insert "to phone Illinois" before "on the moon".

Delete "Who was the first", and delete "to".

The result of each step, and the final answer, are on page 44.

Delete "on the moon".

Move "phone Illinois" before "strong charming man".

Move "charming" to before "strong" and delete "ing".

The answer to the first question is hidden in the sentence. Try to find it.

Delete the surrounding letters to make it appear on your screen.

Opposites

Try to change CURRIED CHICKEN to ICE CREAM.
1. Type out CURRIED CHICKEN.
2. Delete URID from CURRIED.
3. Delete CHKN from CHICKEN.
4. Add AM to first word.
5. Switch words round.

Write your own limerick

There was a young robot called Mike,
Who came with a crash off his bike,
His ribs were of tin,
And they made such a din,
That from then on he rode on a trike.

Replace Mike, bike and trike with three rhyming words, e.g. Dan, van and man. Find two rhyming words to replace tin and din, such as mud and thud. See how many limericks you can make up.

Whodunnit?

To find out "whodunnit", type out the following passages and then use your markers* to carry out the instructions beneath each one.

A) In the snow outside was (the holly tree)[1] of footprints coming from[4] at the end of the lawn to (a set)[3]. They (the open French windows)[2] seemed to go back up the garden, but stopped there.

Swap 2 and 3, swap 3 and 1, move 1 to 4.

B) "A very clever trick," said Inspector Blair to himself (as he built a snowman)[1]. He (looked carefully)[2] into the study and (strode)[3] at everyone's shoes. "What a crafty villain to have got away!", grunted (Mrs Pimple, her niece Felicity and)[4] Major Hogg.

Delete 1, swap 2 and 3, delete 4.

C) "My (chocolate custard)[1] diamonds," she cried. "They've stolen my (chocolate custard)[2] diamonds!"
"Nobody move!" shouted (the open French windows)[3] as he ran (Inspector Blair)[5] (through)[4].

Delete 1 and 2, swap 5 and 3, move 3 to 4.

D) It was a dark and stormy (study)[1]. Four (cards)[3] were sitting playing (people)[4] in Major Hogg's (night)[2].

Swap 1 and 2, swap 3 and 4.

F) "Not crafty enough," said (the Major's snow-covered shoes)[1] looking at (the Major's wrists)[2]. In one quick move he snapped a pair of handcuffs round (Felicity and Mrs Pimple)[3] (Inspector Blair)[4] and plucked a shining necklace from his pocket.

Delete 3, swap 4 and 1, swap 1 and 2.

E) Suddenly (her throat)[1] went out and somebody screamed. When they went on again, Mrs Pimple was lying on (the lights)[2] clutching (the floor)[3].

Swap 3 and 2, swap 2 and 1.

When you have followed the instructions for each section, put them in the following order: DECABF.

See page 18 for how to use markers.

Shaping your text

Before you print it out, you may want to change the appearance of your text by lining up edges, dividing it into pages, creating margins and so on. This is called formatting. On these two pages, you can read about different ways of formatting your text. Your manual will show you which keys or commands to use.

On-screen formatting

Your formatting instructions appear either in the margin or on the format line at the top or bottom of the screen.

With some word processors, what you see on your document screen looks the same as what finally gets printed out. This is called on-screen formatting.

Embedded commands

Embedded commands may be in a different colour or in brackets. They will not be printed out.

Other word processors only put your formatting commands into effect when you print out your text. You type your formatting instructions in the body of the text. They are called embedded commands. There may be a menu option which shows you a picture of what the printed text will look like, called a preview. You cannot edit the text while it is being previewed.

Margins

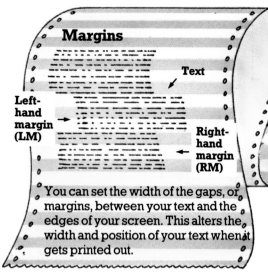

Left-hand margin (LM)

Text

Right-hand margin (RM)

You can set the width of the gaps, or margins, between your text and the edges of your screen. This alters the width and position of your text when it gets printed out.

Setting margins

If your word processor uses embedded commands, you usually tell it how many character spaces in from the edge of the screen you want each margin to be (e.g. LM 10, RM 70).

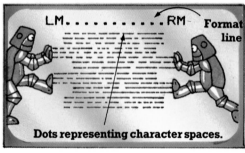

LM . . . . RM   Format line

Dots representing character spaces.

With on-screen formatting you can alter the width of the margins by adjusting the positions of the symbols representing the margins on the format line.

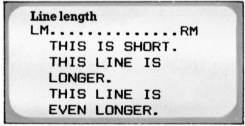

Line length
```
LM . . . . . . . . . . . . . . RM
    THIS IS SHORT.
    THIS LINE IS
    LONGER.
    THIS LINE IS
    EVEN LONGER.
```

With many word processors, you change your line length and adjust the right-hand margin with the same command. Line lengths can help if you want your text, when printed out, to fill a specific area.

Tabs

As well as margins, you can set other points to start lines, columns and different parts of your text, called tabs.

Setting tabs

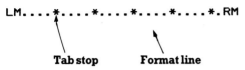

```
LM....*....*....*....*....*.RM
```

Tab stop   **Format line**

Some computers have fixed tab stops, positioned at intervals of five to ten character spaces across the screen. These are shown on the format line as numbers or symbols. By pressing the TAB key, or control code, you can move the cursor to the next TAB position on the line. You can also set your own TAB positions. This is usually done by moving the tab stops on your format line to different places, or typing in an embedded command.

New paragraphs   **Indent**

Using a TAB at the beginning of a new paragraph saves you time typing spaces to indent the first line.

Columns	
LM*........*...RM	
apple	pig
orange	cow
pear	hen
peach	horse

If you have columns to type, tabs will fix the starting point of each one. This will give your columns a neat, straight appearance, and save you a lot of time.

Decimal tabs	
...*.......*...	
34.1	3.9
29.22	2.67
114.8	1.12
2.96	34.2
7.7	4.9

If you want to type columns of figures, decimal tabs line up the decimal points beneath one another.

Level sides

Text before justification.   **Uneven, or ragged edge.**   **Text after justification.**

Most word processors can line up text against the right-hand margin as well as the left, so that both sides are straight. This is called justification. They do this by adjusting the spaces between words.

Line spacing

You can alter spaces between lines by pressing a function key, control code or typed command with the number of lines you want left blank between each line of typing. This is usually between one and three line spaces, like on a typewriter.

Making pages

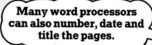

Many word processors can also number, date and title the pages.

You can divide large amounts of text into pages. You tell the word processor the size of the sheets of paper you are using, i.e. how many printed lines can fit on them, and then tell it how many lines you want left blank at the top and bottom. For instance, top and bottom spaces of ten lines each on a 70 line page will give you 50 lines of text per page.

Pitch

The number of characters your printer can print per inch or 2.5 centimetres is called pitch.* Some word processors allow you to change the pitch to squash letters up or space them out. Your manual will show you how to do this.

23

*10 pitch means 10 characters per inch or 2.5 centimetres.

Formatting practice

Here are some games and puzzles to help you practise formatting your text, as described on the last two pages. With on-screen formatting, you can see the results on your screen as you type. With embedded commands, you can check the results by previewing your text or by printing it out. Try to follow the instructions carefully. Only use your space bar where you are told to.

How to do the puzzles

The instructions for some of the puzzles consist of a set of symbols. These stand for formatting commands, as follows:

LM – Set left margin (e.g. LM3 – set your left margin three spaces in from the edge of the screen).

LL – Set line length (e.g. LL60 – set your line length to 60 characters).

C – Type any character (e.g. 35C – type 35 characters, such as 'X').

S – Type a space (e.g. 20S – type 20 spaces).

PR – Press RETURN key.

Name the robot

Set your margins as follows and type out the characters listed, with no spaces. The robot's name will appear on your screen.
PR, LM10, PR; 40C, PR, repeat twice; 20C, PR, repeat 4 times; 40C, PR, repeat twice; 20C, PR, repeat 9 times; LM20, PR; 20C, PR, repeat 9 times; LM10, PR; 20C, PR, repeat 6 times; 40C, PR, repeat twice.

This puzzle will not work on a screen less than 60 characters wide.

A conversation

Complete the following conversation, by putting your own words in the gaps. Start new paragraphs where you think it needs them. Press your RETURN key to start a new line, and then your TAB key. (Line length 50, left margin 0.)

"Do your like _," asked the _. "Certainly _," replied _. "But what about _ and _?" said _. "That is for _, and anyway I _!"

Lists

Set your tabs at intervals of ten characters. Type the following words, pressing your TAB key between each word and RETURN at the end of each line. (Line length 40, left margin 0.)

butter	truck	desert	kangaroo
banjo	tender	drip	king
bend	trade	dream	kitten
blues	tricks	dancing	kennel

If you change your tabs, some word processors move the columns. Others need extra commands to do this.

Decimal tabs

23·4   52·39   0·31   2·4   6·6
90·8   7·62   1000·01   77   3·521

If your word processor has decimal tabs, see if you can use them to arrange these figures in a column with the decimal points directly beneath each other.

Straight sides

Complete this story by making up words to put in the blank spaces. When you have finished, justify the right margin. (Line length 40, left margin 0.)

Once upon a _ there was a _ which lived in a _. The only _ it had was a _ which couldn't stop _. It got so _ that one day the _ went to a _. When it _ it to the _ it seemed to _. Suddenly it _, and the whole _ went completely _. From that day onwards, they lived in utter _.

Which animal?

This puzzle will help you practise changing the space between lines. If you follow these instructions, an animal's face will appear on your screen. Which animal is it? LS means set your line space to the number of lines specified, e.g. LS4 is four lines long. The puzzle will not work on systems without line spacing commands of up to four lines.

LS1, LL40, LM0, PR, PR, PR; 8S, 1C, 25S, 1C, PR; 7S, 3C, 23S, 3C, PR; 6S, 5C, 21S, 5C, PR; 6S, 7C, 17S, 7C, PR; 6S, 8C, 15S, 8C, PR; 6S, 5C, 8S, 5C, 8S, 5C, PR; 6S, 2C, 27S, 2C, PR; LS4, PR; LS1, 12S, 4C, 11S, 4C, PR; 13S, 5C, 7S, 5C, PR; 15S, 3C, 7S, 3C, PR; LS3, PR; LS1, 19S, IC, 3S, IC, PR; 19S, 2C, 1S, 2C, PR; 21S, 1C, PR; 21S, 1C, PR; 15S, 1C, 4S, 1C, 1S, 1C, 4S, 1C, PR; 16S, 4C, 3S, 4C, PR; LS2, PR; LS1, 20S, 3C, PR, PR.

Checkmate

If you follow these instructions a chess board will appear on your screen. The question is: who won, black or white? These pieces are shown as follows: White Knight (WKN), Black King (BK), White Rook (WR), White Queen (WQ), Black Queen (BQ), White King (WK). The answer, plus the rules of chess, are on page 45.*

1. LM10, LL65; Set tabs at 15, 21, 27, 33, 39, 45, 51, 57, PR.
2. Tab, S, tab, 6C, S, tab, 6C, S, tab, 6C, S, tab, 6C, PR.
3. Repeat line 2 twice.
4. Tab, 6C, S, tab, 6C, S, tab, 6C, S, tab, 6C, PR.
5. Repeat line 4 twice.
6. Repeat line 2 three times.
7. Repeat line 4 once.
8. Tab, 6C, S, tab, 6C, S, tab, 1C, S, type WKN, 1C, S, tab, 6C, PR.
9. Repeat line 4 once.
10. Repeat line 2 three times.
11. Repeat line 4 once.
12. Tab, 6C, S, tab, 6C, S, tab, 6C, 2S, type WQ, 2S, 6C, PR.
13. Repeat line 4 once.
14. Repeat line 2 once.
15. Tab, S, tab, 1C, S, type BQ, S, 1C, S, tab, 6C, S, tab, 6C, 2S, type BK, 2S, 6C, PR.
16. Repeat line 2: repeat line 4.
17. Tab, 6C, S, tab, 6C, 2S, type WK, 2S, 6C, S, tab, 6C, 2S, type WR, 2S, PR.
18. Repeat line 4 once.

Pitch

When you have tried some of these puzzles, alter the pitch on your word processor to see how it changes the appearance of your text, and the space it takes up.

Pages

When you have typed out a lot of text, try dividing it into pages. Choose your page size by making the total number of lines left blank at the top and bottom the same as your age.

Headings and numbers

Now try numbering and putting a title on each page, using your numbering and heading codes. If your word processor has a centering code, use it to make your headings central.

This puzzle will not work on systems without an 80 character screen format.

Storing information

These pages show you how to store or save what you have typed on to a tape or a disk and how to load it back into your word processor. You can find out about the basic equipment you can use (a disk drive or cassette recorder) on pages 10-11. There is more about different kinds of disks and disk drives below.

Disks and disk drives

There are several different kinds of disk drive. Check before you buy one that it will work with your computer. The type of disk you use depends on the type of disk drive, and your computer's disk operating system (DOS)*. Some of the terms used to describe disk drives and disks are explained here.

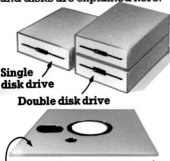

Single disk drive

Double disk drive

A single disk drive takes one disk. A double disk drive can take two, which makes it easier to copy and merge batches of text, or files.

Double-sided disks store information on both sides.

A single-sided disk drive takes single-sided disks, which store information on one side only. A double-sided disk drive takes disks which can store files on both sides.

Depending on your word processor's DOS, you may be able to use double-density disks which store twice the amount of information as single-density disks.

Formatting disks

Concentric tracks

Sector

A disk needs to be divided up into areas called tracks and sectors before information can be stored on it. This is called formatting the disk. Some disks come with these areas already marked on them by a series of holes. These are hard-sectored disks.

With other disks you need to format them yourself, using a special formatting program which divides the disk magnetically. These are called soft-sectored disks. A formatting program is usually supplied on a disk when you buy a disk drive.

Disk operating systems are explained on page 10.

Saving and loading

SAVE

LOAD

To store a file, you press the SAVE key, or type SAVE, followed by the name of your file.

To load a file you have saved on a disk or tape into your word processor, you type out the LOAD command and the name of the file you want.

Filenames

It helps to give your file a name that will remind you what it contains, for example:

WHERE? (File of addresses.)
WHEN? (File of important dates, birthdays, anniversaries etc.)

On most word processors you can use letters and numbers for your filenames, but hyphens instead of spaces. If you have several files on one subject you can give them the same name with different numbers or letters at the end.

JOKES-1, JOKES-2, JOKES-3 (Files of jokes.)
SONGS-A, SONGS-B, SONGS-C (Files of songs.)

Most word processors will not take filenames longer than 14 letters.

Catalogues

Part of a disk is reserved for a catalogue or index containing the names of all the files stored on it. If you type out the word processor's catalogue command, it will list all the filenames on the screen.

Similarly, you can find out the names of files stored on a tape, but your word processor has to wind all the way through it, listing each filename at the start of each file. You can find out your word processor's catalogue command from your manual.

Filename	Operator	Size	Created
Bills-a	J. Grimm	4	4-5-85
Desserts-a	I. C. Ream	15	7-9-85
Motorcycles-4	G. Wheely	2	1-8-85

Bytes* remaining on disk 173 (87%).

Some catalogues show you items such as the size of the file in pages or bytes*, the date it was stored, the name of the person who stored it and the amount of space left on the disk.

Altering files

You can alter, or revise a file you have stored by loading it into the word processor and changing it. You can then save the new version under the same filename. It replaces the old one. On some word processors you use UPDATE instead of SAVE to store a new version of an old file.

*One byte is equivalent to one character.

Protecting files

On some word processors you can protect or lock files by typing in a command. This means you cannot save a new or altered file with the same filename on top of a locked file without first unlocking it. This prevents you from altering or overwriting a file by mistake.

Deleting files

You can delete files you no longer need, to leave more room on the disk. You can find the "file delete" command in your manual.

Back-ups

It is a good idea to make a copy on a separate disk of each file you save, called a back-up copy. This means that if you accidentally delete a file, or the first disk gets damaged, you have not lost the file altogether.

Labelling disks

You can label disks to remind you what is stored on them, e.g. Recipes, or Letters. Put a sticky label on the disk and use a soft felt tip pen to write on it, so you don't damage the disk.

Remember

1. Never touch the shiny part of a disk.
2. Do not put a disk in or take it out while the drive is working.
3. Keep your disks in their paper sleeves when not in use.
4. Store disks upright in a box to protect them.

27

Printing

Here you can read about how to choose a printer to buy and how to use it. Different types of printer are described on pages 10-11.

Choosing a printer

When you buy a printer you should choose one to suit your needs. The more expensive ones usually produce better quality print.

A cheap thermal printer probably does not produce good enough print for word processing, unless it is just for your own use at home.

A B C

This is thermal print.

A B C

This is dot matrix print.

For printing letters, circulars, essays and so on, you may prefer a dot matrix printer, which prints more clearly. The more expensive ones are as good as a typewriter.

For professional use, or to make very smart copies, you probably need a daisy wheel or golfball printer, which are even more expensive.

A B C

This is daisy wheel print.

Printer interfaces

To make a printer work, your word processor needs a printer interface. Dedicated word processors have them built in and so do some home computers. If you need one, you can get it fitted by a dealer. Many printers and computers use a type of interface called Centronics. Remember that the printer and computer need the same kind of interface in order to work together.

Other things you need

Here are some of the other things you need in order to use your printer.

Lead

Make sure that a lead to connect the printer to the word processor is supplied with the printer.

Paper

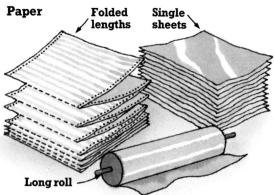

Folded lengths
Single sheets
Long roll

Friction-feed printers can take single sheets or rolls of paper. Pin-feed printers use lengths of folded paper divided into sheets by perforated lines. Some printers can use all three kinds of paper.

Ribbon

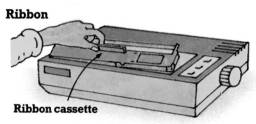

Ribbon cassette

There are two types of printer ribbon. Fabric ribbon is tough and long-lasting, but produces slightly blurry print. Carbon ribbon produces crisp, high quality print. It is fragile, though, and costs more than fabric ribbon.

You can easily swap carbon and fabric ribbon around in your printer, as they are kept in cassettes. You could use carbon ribbon for very tidy print-outs, and fabric ribbon for drafts and copies.

Special printer commands

Many word processors have extra commands just for the printer. You type these in like ordinary commands, but you cannot see their effect until your text is printed out. Here are some examples.

Headings and page numbers

You can instruct the printer to print a heading and page number on each page as it prints them out.

Underlining and different type styles

You can make some printers underline certain words, or print them in a different type style (e.g. bold.*) You type in a code at the beginning and end of the group of words.

```
43        Chapter 4

   "I saw forty
 flying turtles
 through my window
 yesterday!"
   "I saw forty
 flying turtles
 feeding foxes
 through my window
 yesterday!"
   "I saw forty
 feeding foxes
 through my window
 yesterday!"
```

Proportional spacing

On the screen, each letter takes up the same amount of space. If you look at the words in this book you can see that some letters take up more space than others. This is called proportional spacing. Some printers can print out text in this way. It looks more professional. In the picture on the left, for example, "w" takes up more space than "i", in "window".

Printing out text

When you type the PRINT command on your word processor, your printer will start printing the file that is currently in your word processor's memory.

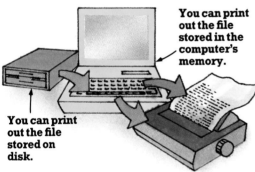

You can print out the file stored in the computer's memory.

You can print out the file stored on disk.

Some word processors let you print out files stored on a tape or disk, without affecting the file in the memory.

Some have another command, e.g. SHEETS, for printing on separate sheets. This makes the printer stop at the end of each page so you can put in a new sheet of paper.

You can usually tell a printer to type out a certain number of copies.

Sheet feeder

If you need lots of copies printed on single sheets, you can buy a sheet feeder which loads sheets into the printer one by one.

Warning signals

Your printer usually warns you with a signal if the paper is about to run out, or if the ribbon is wearing out.

Altering typefaces during printing

You may want to change your character style, or typeface, in the middle of printing, e.g. for quotes, footnotes and so on. You can do this on some daisy wheel printers by programming a special "stop" command into your text. This makes the printer stop when it reaches it, and allows you to change the print head.

29

*There is an example of bold type on page 11.

Other things word processors can do

Most of the standard things word processors can do have already been covered in this book. On this page are some further useful functions. Your manual will tell you if your word processor can do these things.

Wraparound

As you type in your text, some words may be too long to fit at the end of a line. Most word processors automatically take the whole word over to the beginning of the next line. This is called "word wrap", or "wraparound".

```
Dear Sir,

        I am avoiding your
arithmetic course because I am aller-
gic to arithmetic. As I was born on
6 June, I am a Gemini, and as you
know, we are all allergic to
arithmetic.
```

Connecting spaces

Some groups of words, such as dates, should not be split up over two lines. The word processor may have a special space key or code you can use between such words, instead of the space bar, which tells it to keep the words on the same line.

Hyphens

Some systems let you hyphenate long words at the end of a line, instead of taking the whole word over to the next line. The word processor stops at the end of the line so you can type in a hyphen if you want to.

If you readjust the text, and the word is pushed into the middle of a line, the hyphen is automatically deleted.

Widows and orphans

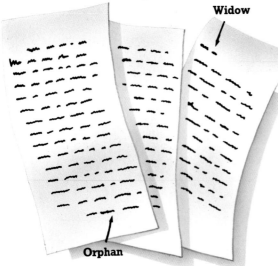

Widow

Orphan

When your word processor divides text into pages, an odd word or line can get left behind on the last page, called an orphan, or be moved on to the next page, called a widow. Some machines automatically adjust the paging to avoid this, by moving a widow back to the previous page, or an orphan on to the next page.

Stop codes

```
Dear (Stop code),
        Thank you for your enquiry
about our holidays in (Stop code). I
enclose the details.
```

You can make the cursor position itself in the middle of the text when you load a file, instead of at the beginning. This is useful for things like standard letters, where you want to type in a name, or add sentences in the middle. You insert "stop codes" where you want the cursor to jump to.

Date codes

Some word processors have a key you press to print out the date so that you do not have to type it out each time. You give the machine the correct date and after that you just press the date key or code. Other machines have clocks inside them, and when you press the date key they print out the current date automatically.

Glossary

```
The St chased the Bt through the dark
forest until night fell.

St Stegosaurus
Pt Pterodactylus
Dp Diplodocus
Ar Archaeopteryx
Bt Brontosaurus
```

Instead of typing long or difficult words, you can store them in a "glossary", and replace them with labels of two or three letters. You type the labels into your text instead of the words. When you have finished typing, you press the glossary function keys and the correct words replace the labels throughout your text.

Help

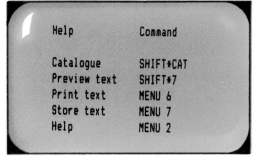

```
Help            Command

Catalogue       SHIFT*CAT
Preview text    SHIFT*7
Print text      MENU 6
Store text      MENU 7
Help            MENU 2
```

Some systems can show you a list of the word processor's main command codes on the screen, along with what each one does. This can be a real help while you are learning to use your word processor. You press the help key or code to display the list on the screen.

Home key

```
■
Suddenly, as if by magic, she found
herself home again sitting in that
rocking chair. It was all there... the
parrot, the smell of the pigs, the dirty
washing, her grandfather combing his
beard.
```

When you press this key, the cursor returns to the beginning of your document. This can save you time when you are formatting or checking through your text.

Spelling checker

```
He went to recieve the J.B. Belling
Award for spelling.
```

This is like a stored dictionary. It checks your spelling against the words in its dictionary and signals any word that you have spelt wrong.

Indents

```
Beneath the statue of dissolving
spaghetti, hailed by art critics to be a
masterpiece, was a metal plaque.

    "You can fool half the people
    all of the time; you can fool all
    of the people half of the time:
    but you can't fool all of the
    people all of the time."
```

If you want to set a block of text in from the left-hand margin you can use the Indent code at the start of the block and cancel it at the end. This saves you having to use TAB commands at the start of every line.

Arithmetic

```
    27      45      67
    38      30       8
    10      32       3
    12      23      11
    44      88      96
    33      27      71
    -----------------
   164     245     256
```

Some systems can add up columns of figures, and may do other simple arithmetic.

31

Here is a game which will help you practise typing and using the word processing functions you have read about so far. Imagine you are a newspaper editor. This is a diary you keep on a typical day and a story from a reporter in the form of notes. Follow the instructions in italics to prepare the story for publication.

1.00p.m. Received story from freelance reporter.

This guy's stuff is usually hot!

Set top space at 5, left margin at 7, line length 36.

2.00p.m. Could be a smash. Face looks familiar.

Follow the instructions below to make a face appear on the screen. For the meaning of the codes turn to page 24. RE means repeat line.

1. 11S,14C,PR
2. 9S,18C,PR
3. 7S,22C,PR
4. 6S,3C,1S,14C,2S,3C,PR
5. 6S,2C,5S,10C,4S,3C,PR
6. 5S,3C,8S,3C,8S,3C,PR

7. 5S,2C,3S,5C,5S,5C,3S,2C,PR
8. 5S,1C,2S,9C,1S,9C,2S,1C,PR
9. 5S,7C,1S,9C,1S,8C,PR
10. 4S,3C,1S,19C,1S,3C,PR
11. 3S,4C,2S,7C,3S,7C,2S,4C,PR
12. 2S,1C,2S,2C,21S,2C,2S,1C,PR,RE
13. 3S,1C,10S,1C,5S,1C,10S,1C,PR
14. 4S,2C,8S,1C,5S,1C,8C,2C,PR
15. 15S,5C,7S,1C,PR
16. 7S,1C,3S,6C,1S,6C,PR
17. 14S,3C,1S,3C,6S,1C,PR
18. 8S,1C,PR
19. 9S,1C,16S,1C,PR
20. 10S,1C,12S,1C,PR
21. 13S,1C,2S,1C,3S,1C,PR

3.30p.m. Reporter's story needs heavy editing.

At ? on Main Street, death on the road was narrowly avoided in yet another bicycle collision between Mrs Whatshername and Mr Blank. Mrs Whatshername's bag of baked beans, vanilla ice cream and bananas was scattered over the pavement.

Type out story. Replace ? with 11a.m. Delete all food names and replace with "shopping".

4.30p.m. Visit from editor of rival newspaper.

Store entire text.

5.30p.m. Rival editor leaves.

Slim, blond Mr Blank (23), protested, "It's not my fault!" Mrs Whatshername retorted with unrepeatable words.

Reload entire text. Continue typing story. Insert "Birdlike, delicate" before "Mrs". Replace everything after "retorted" with "Rubbish!"

30p.m. News Editor visits demanding to see statistics of previous bicycle crashes.

Statistics for previous collisions between aforementioned persons.

Year	1983	1984	1985
Collisions	25	72	46
New bikes	11	65	45

Use tab keys to type out statistics.

7.30p.m. Sent out for peanut butter sandwiches.

A crowd soon gathered. Constable Jones took statements from witnesses. One of them, a Mr. Milton P. Stickleback Jnr. said, "I saw absolutely nothing".

Continue typing story. Delete last sentence.

30p.m. I knew I recognized that face!

Suddenly, one of the country's most dangerous men, Mario Marinetti, rushed out of the nearby bank. He was dumbfounded by the group of policemen on hand.

Continue typing story.

9.30p.m. Visit from News Editor. Punchy headline needed . . . "Bicycle Barricade"?

Think of a headline. Insert it at top centre of page. Underline headline and change "Mario Marinetti" to bold.

30p.m. What a scoop!

As he swerved to avoid them, he slipped on one of Mrs Whatshername's bananas, and into the hands of the law. All charges against the cyclists are being withdrawn.

Type out story. Justify all text after picture.

11.30p.m. Get calls from both cyclists.

Use search and replace keys to swap Whatshername for Phyllis Mcgraw and Blank for Stanley Stonewall.

READ ALL ABOUT IT!

5p.m. Call from Chief. Deadline brought forward to 12.00. HELP!

Set page length. Number pages.

11.55p.m. Five minutes to deadline.

Check formatting. Save back-up copy.

12.00a.m. Rush story off to print room.

Print out picture and story.

EXTRA

EDITOR COLLAPSES

Looking after your machine and yourself

If you look after your word processor by keeping it clean and cutting down on wear and tear, it will work more efficiently and last longer. There are some guidelines to help you on this page.

Some people who work all day at a word processor may suffer from certain side effects, such as backache or eyestrain. You can find out how to avoid these on the opposite page. Using a word processor for an hour or two at a time is unlikely to affect you at all.

Keeping your word processor clean

★ It is important to keep your machine clean. Dust and crumbs can get inside and clog up the works.
★ The screen attracts dust, making it harder to read, so clean it regularly.
★ Every time you use your disk drive, oxide from the disk rubs off on the sensitive head inside it. This may eventually stop it working. You can clean this head with a special cleaning disk and fluid.

Things to remember

Switch everything off when you have finished using your machine.

Do not remove or replace a disk while the disk drive is working.

Move your computer and disk drive as little as possible, as they are fragile. If you carry a disk drive about, leave a disk inside it to support its head.

Avoid placing disks near instruments with magnetic fields like TVs, radios, hi-fis or telephones, as this may erase the data on them.

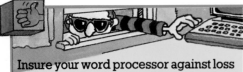

Insure your word processor against loss or damage. Remember to make back-up copies of your disks.

Spilling food or drink on your keyboard can ruin the electronic contacts.

Repairs and maintenance

When you buy a word processor, check that it has a guarantee for at least a year. If it breaks down, take it back for repair to the shop where you bought it.

With some machines you can buy a service contract. This means that for a fixed yearly payment, your word processor will be repaired free, whenever it breaks down. This is useful for businesses which use lots of word processors. For your own machine it is generally cheaper to get it repaired at a shop. The cost of maintenance usually averages out at about ½ to 1% of the original cost of the machine per month.

Word processors and side effects

The side effects suffered by people who use word processors continuously are often caused by the way they sit and the strain of staring at a screen for long periods of time. Here are some ways to prevent them.

Aching muscles

Aches and pains in your back, neck and shoulders are usually caused by sitting badly and staying in the same position for a long time. The picture shows how you should arrange your equipment and the kind of chair you should use.

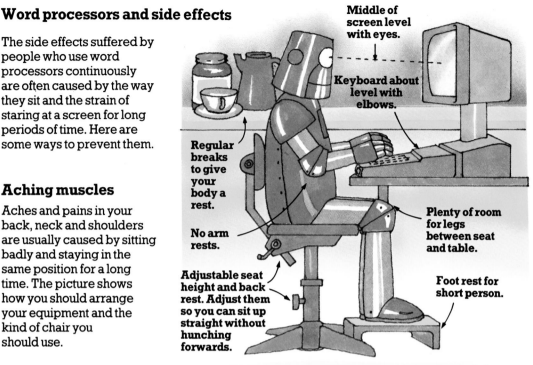

Middle of screen level with eyes.

Keyboard about level with elbows.

Regular breaks to give your body a rest.

No arm rests.

Adjustable seat height and back rest. Adjust them so you can sit up straight without hunching forwards.

Plenty of room for legs between seat and table.

Foot rest for short person.

Eye strain

Sore or tired eyes, headaches and difficulty in focusing may be caused by looking at a screen for hours on end. People who wear glasses, or are on certain drugs, may suffer more than others.

Things which contribute to eye strain are reflections of bright lights on the screen (glare), small character size, poor character quality and an over-bright screen display. The picture shows you ways to avoid eye strain.

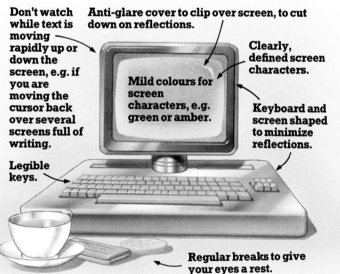

Don't watch while text is moving rapidly up or down the screen, e.g. if you are moving the cursor back over several screens full of writing.

Anti-glare cover to clip over screen, to cut down on reflections.

Clearly, defined screen characters.

Mild colours for screen characters, e.g. green or amber.

Keyboard and screen shaped to minimize reflections.

Legible keys.

Regular breaks to give your eyes a rest.

Epilepsy

Using word processors may cause fits in certain kinds of epileptics. This may be due to a flickering screen or flashing cursor. A better quality screen should have a more stable display. A slow blinking or non-flashing cursor may also help.

Stress

Using a word processor to carry out repetitive, boring work can cause symptoms such as tension and headaches. Regular breaks and variation in work can help. A computer that does not work properly can also be stressful, and should be changed.

Radiation

Scientists are researching whether the minute amounts of radiation given off by the screen may cause headaches, or even severe eye disorders. They think that bad posture and eye strain are more likely to be the cause, but investigation is continuing.

Buying your own word processor

On these two pages, you can read how to go about choosing and buying a word processor. Below are some questions to ask yourself, which may help you choose. On the following pages there is a Buyer's Guide which describes some of the most commonly used word processors and software.

Cost

A cheap word processing program on cassette may cost about the same as a couple of computer games.

The most expensive dedicated word processors cost about the same as a small new car.

How much money are you prepared to pay for a word processor? This may limit your choice of machines immediately.

Type of machine

Do you want a dedicated word processor, or a microcomputer with word processing software?*

Command system and formatting

What kind of command system do you want on your machine?* Menus and function keys may help you to work faster, but may increase the cost of the system.

You can use embedded commands for formatting letters and so on, but you may need on-screen formatting for more complicated documents.

Memory size

A home computer with a 32K memory and a word processing program can hold about 3,500 words at once.

What size of memory do you need? If you are going to be working on large amounts of information, you will probably need a machine with at least 32K.

Ease and comfort of use

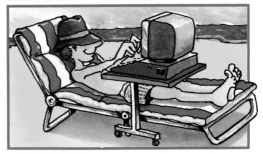

How often are you going to use your word processor? If you plan to use it all day long, it may be worth paying more for a high quality screen display and a strong keyboard with keys that are easy to press.

Other equipment

What type of hardware (i.e. storage equipment, printer and screen) would you like to use with a word processor? Cassette recorders may suit many home computer users. Disks and disk drives are faster and more efficient but cost more (see pages 10-11). If you plan to use the machine frequently, a double disk drive with double-sided disks is the most convenient.

Daisy wheel | Dot matrix | Thermal

Is the quality of print from the printer important to you, or is it just for your own use (see pages 28-29)?

Screen

A monitor is a screen especially designed to work with a computer.

What kind of screen do you want? You can use a television as a screen display with a home computer, but the picture is blurred and flickery, and it is a strain to look at for long. A monitor gives a steadier screen display.

*For information about command systems see pages 16-17.

Word processing needs

Here are some of the qualities that different people might find most useful in word processors.

Journalist

Dedicated word processor. Easy editing. On-screen formatting. Spelling checker. Disk system for speed. Fast printer.

Solicitor's secretary

Good on-screen formatting for complicated documents. Paging and merging facilities. Glossary. High quality printer and sheet feeder.

Household user

Home computer with facilities for other software, such as games. Possibly simple arithmetic for household budgets. Cassette system for economy.

Author

Easy editing. Page numbering and hyphenating. Good screen display.

Partner of a small business

A microcomputer that can take accounting software. Stop code. Decimal tabs. Disk system. Sheet feeder.

Shopping guidelines

Here are some guidelines to follow when shopping for a word processor.

1. Ask for a demonstration of any machine you plan to buy, as well as trying it out yourself. Ask about specific functions such as editing and formatting facilities. Salesmen may not always give you very reliable advice, so try to find the expert in the shop. It is usually best to make an appointment if you plan to spend a lot of money.

2. If you want to buy a microcomputer, it may be best to choose a good word processing program first, and a computer that works with it afterwards.

3. Find out how much you are going to have to spend on additional hardware, such as a printer and a disk drive.

4. Check the word processor's guarantee, which should last at least a year, and on service facilities.

5. Listen to recommendations from friends or contacts with similar needs. Look for reviews in computer magazines.

6. Always shop around and look for discounts. Compare the prices of makes with similar facilities.

The differences between them are described on pages 8-9.

Software buyer's guide

On the next two pages is a chart showing some of the word processing software available. The chart starts with the cheaper software packages (for home users or small businesses) and goes up to the more expensive ones. Some of those over the page are for large office computers. This chart shows a selection of each program's facilities but does not list everything they can do. You can find out the meaning of the abbreviations used in the chart in the key opposite.

Key

A	Arithmetic (page 31).
B	Bold (page 29).
EC	Embedded commands (page 22).
Ex	On-screen formatting excluding right-hand justification (RHJ), bold (B), underlining (U), etc.
He	Help screen (page 31).
Ho	Home key (page 31).
Hy	Hyphens (page 30).
M	Merging (page 19).
OSF	On-screen formatting (page 22).
O	Optional facility.
P	On printer, but not on screen.
Sp	Spelling (page 31).
S	Depending on system being used.
U	Underlining (page 29).
WO	Widows and orphans (page 30).
Wr	Wraparound (page 30).

Name and manufacturer	Software runs on:	Software supplied on tape, disk or chip	Office or home use	Facilities include:	Command system	Other features include:
Wordpro (Wego Computers)	Commodore 64	Disk	Home	Sp(O) Hy A(O) WO M B Ho EC	Command codes.	Easy to learn.
View (Acornsoft)	BBC Micro, Electron.	Tape, disk or chip.	Home and office.	Sp(O) Hy A(O) WO M B Ho U OSF (Ex B+U)	Command codes, function keys.	Choice between 40 and 80 character screen size.
Wordwise Plus (Computer Concepts)	BBC Micro.	Chip	Home and office.	M A Sp(O) Ho B(P) Wr U(P) EC	Menu, function keys and command codes.	Option to add different functions according to user's needs.

Product	Computer	Storage	Use	Codes	Input	Notes
Edword (Clwyd Technics Ltd.)	BBC Micro, Electron.	Chip	Home. Used a lot in schools.	Wr B U Ho Hy OSF	Menu and function keys.	Originally designed by teachers for pupils, so easy to use.
Merlin Scribe (Merlin Computer Products)	BBC Micro.	Chip or disk.	Home and office.	Wr Ho U M(O) Hy A(O) OSF (Ex Hy)	Menu and function keys.	Designed for first time user. Large memory. Can create very large documents.
Tasword 2 (Tasman)	Spectrum.	Tape or chip in cartridge.	Home	M(O) Ho B(P) He U(P) Wr OSF	Menu and function keys.	Wide screen, showing 64 characters per line.
Tasword 464D (Tasman)	Amstrad CPC 464, Amstrad 664.	Disk	Home and office.	He Ho M Wr B(P) Sp U(P) OSF	Menu and function keys.	Access to second character set which contains special symbols and continental characters.
Scripsit (Tandy)	TRS 80 Colour Computer.	Disk or chip in cartridge.	Home	W B(P) Hy U(P) Ho He OSF (Ex RH])	Menu and command codes.	Displays characters in three different colours on screen (orange, green and brown).
Atari Writer (Atari)	All Atari 8-bit micros.	Chip in cartridge.	Home and office.	M Ho B(P) Wr U(P) S(D) EC	Menu, command codes and a few function keys.	Formatting takes place after text has been created.

Name and manufacturer	Software runs on:	Software supplied on tape, disk or chip	Office or home use	Facilities include:	Command system	Other features include:
Apple Writer (Apple)	Apple 11E, Apple 11C.	Disk	Home and small business.	B Wr U He Ho M OSF (Ex RHJ)	Menu and command codes.	Batch processing of large files and documents.
Perfect Writer (Thorn EMI)	IBM PC and compatibles, Apple 11E and 11C.	Disk	Office. Used a lot in universities and by authors.	M(O) Sp B Wr U He Ho OSF or EC	Menu, command codes or function keys.	Has prompt commands which tell you what to do next.
Quill, QL version (Psion)	Comes with Sinclair QL	Chip in cartridge.	Home and office.	Wr Hy He B Ho U OSF	Menu and function keys.	Contains the useful features of a professional word processor but is easy to use.
Quill, Xchange version (Psion)	IBM PC, XT, AT, ACT Apricot, Apricot X1, Kennet, ICL OPD, Commodore PC, Torch Graduate, Olivetti M24 and M21, Compaq.	Disk or chip.	Office	M He B Hy U Wr Ho OSF	Menu and function keys.	Very similar to Xchange version but fewer facilities.
Wordcraft, Commodore version (Dataview)	Commodore 64	Disk	Home and small business.	M Ho Hy Wr B U OSF	Function keys and command codes. Separate command and edit mode.	Special prompts appear on screen to help user.
Wordcraft (Dataview)	IBM PC and compatibles, Olivetti, Apricot.	Disk	Office	M He Hy U B Ho Wr A Sp OSF	As above.	Useful for compiling dictionaries.

Software	Computers	Storage	Used for	Features	Operation	Notes
Superwriter (Sorcim-IUS)	IBM PC and compatibles, ACT Apricot, any CPM* machine.	Disk	Home and office.	M Ho WO Wr B Sp U Hy EC	Menu and function keys.	Can be used on wide range of microcomputers.
Wordstar (Micro-Pro International)	Most 8- and 16-bit microcomputers including IBM, Olivetti, Apple, etc.	Disk	Office	M(O) U Hy Ho Sp(O) Wr B He OSF or EC	Command codes.	Can be used on a wide range of microcomputers.
Spellbinder (Sierra Systems)	IBM and compatibles, ACT Apricot, Future FX, DEC Rainbow, plus other microcomputers.	Disk	Office	M Ho WO Wr Hy A U Sp B He EC	Function keys and command codes. Separate edit and command modes.	Has grammar checker which pulls out sentences without full stops, banned words and so on.
Multimate (Ferrari Software)	IBM PC and compatibles, Corona, Hewlett Packard HP 150, Toshiba, Victor 9000, Zenith 150.	Disk	Office	M Ho WO Wr H A B(S) Sp U(S) He OSF	Menus, command codes and function keys.	Can be programmed to remember small tasks, after doing them once.
Microsoft Word (Microsoft Ltd.)	IBM and compatibles, ACT Apricot, AT, Olivetti, Macintosh, Commodore PC.	Disk	Home and office. Used a lot by authors and other writers.	M Ho WO Wr Hy Sp B He U OSF	Menus, function keys or command codes.	Option of "mouse" (hand held unit to control cursor and select commands on screen).

*CPM is the standard operating system for most 8-bit business computers.

41

Dedicated word processor buyer's guide

Below you can see some of the most commonly used makes of dedicated word processors. The chart shows some of the facilities each one has and the type of printer and disk drive each one uses. The key on the right will help you understand the letters in the chart.

Key

A Arithmetic (page 31).
B Bold (page 29).
CPS Characters per second.
CO Optional communication with other word processors.
Da Date code (page 30).
DM Dot matrix printer (page 11).
DW Daisy wheel printer (page 11).
EM Electronic mail (page 7).
EX On-screen formatting except right-hand justification (RHJ) or double line spacing (DLS).
G Glossary (page 31).
He Help screen (page 31).
Ho Home key (page 31).
Hy Hyphens (page 30).
I Indent (31).
L Laser printer (page 11).
M Merging (page 19).
O Optional facility.
OSF On-screen formatting (page 22).
Sp Spelling (page 31).
SA Stand-alone system (page 8).
SR Shared resource system (page 8).
St Stop code (page 30).
U Underline (page 29).
WO Widows and orphans (page 30).
Wr Wraparound (page 30).

Name, memory size and description	Printer type and speed	Type of disk drive, and disk capacity	Formatting	Type of command system	Facilities include:	Other features include:
ICL DRS 8801 256K* SA or SR, CO, EM.	DW. 35-65 CPS.	Double. 120 A4 pages per disk.	OSF	Function keys and mnemonics**.	A Hy St B I U Da M WO Ho	Facilities for designing forms.
IBM Displaywriter Textpack 4 128-448K. SA or SR, CO, EM.	DW. 60 CPS.	Single or double. 450 A4 pages per disk.	OSF (Ex RHJ & DLS)	Menus, function keys and mnemonics.	A Hy St B I U He M WO Ho Sp Wr	Can merge documents and files, and create charts and graphs.
Philips 5020/WPS 64K, SA, SR(O), CO, EM.	DW and DM. 30-300 CPS. L(O).	Double. 128 A4 pages per disk.	OSF (Ex RHJ)	Function keys and mnemonics.	A Hy St B I U G M WO He Sp Wr Ho	Easily expandable.
Rank Xerox 860 128K, SA or SR, CO, EM	DW. Up to 45 CPS.	Double. 150-300 A4 pages per disk.	OSF	Function keys.	A U Wr Da B WO Hy St I Sp	Option of keyboard with "cat" (see glossary).

Model	Printer	Disk capacity	Input	Commands	Mnemonics	Features
Diamond 7 128K, SA or SR, CO, EM.	DW and DM. 40-340 CPS.	Double. Up to 450 A4 pages per disk.	OSF	Function keys and mnemonics.	A B Wr, Da I WO, Hy U St, Ho M G	Large screen which can show three different formats (½A4, full A4 and twice A4).
Logica 2200 (Also sold as British Telecom Merlin). 256K, SA, CO.	DW and DM. 20-400 CPS.	Double. 100 A4 pages per disk.	OSF (Ex RHJ)	Function keys and mnemonics.	A Ho St, B Hy U, Da I Wr, G M	Easy to draw horizontal and vertical lines, so good for designing forms.
Wang Wangwriter 256-512K, SA or SR, CO.	DW. 20 CPS.	Single or double. 120 A4 pages per disk.	OSF	Menu, function keys.	A Hy U, B I WO, G M Wr, He St	Wide range of facilities. Good for designing forms.
CPT Phoenix Jnr 28-256K, SA or SR, CO, EM.	DW and DM. 20-180 CPS. L(O).	Single or double. 300 A4 pages per disk.	OSF (Ex RHJ)	Function keys and mnemonics.	A Hy St, B I U, Da M WO, G Sp Wr, Ho	Screen designed like piece of A4 paper on typewriter.
AES 7155 256K, SA, SR(O), CO, EM(O).	DW. 20-45 CPS.	Double. Up to 256 A4 pages per disk.	OSF and some embedded commands.	Function keys and mnemonics.	A Hy St, B I U, G M WO, Ho Sp Wr	Easy to adjust position and tilt of screen and keyboard.
Olivetti 2010 ETS 320K, SA, CO, EM(O).	DW and DM. 25-70 CPS.	Double. 180 A4 pages per disk.	OSF	Menu, function keys and mnemonics.	A Hy St, B I U, Da M WO, G Sp Wr, He	Easy on the eye – no blinking or shadowing. Smooth scrolling.
Wordplex 80-4 192K, SA, SR(O), CO, EM(O).	DW and DM. 350-280 CPS. L(O).	Hard disk system. 7,500-8,000 A4 pages per hard disk.	OSF	Function keys and mnemonics.	A Ho Sp, B Hy St, Da I U, G M WO, He(O) Wr	Can perform three tasks at once.

*One kilobyte is 1,024 bytes.

**A mnemonic is an abbreviated command.

Puzzle answers

Page 14

Punctuation

1. "What an extraordinary person!" he said.
2. "Do you really like artichokes, Henry?"
3. "Those nuts – the ones I ate yesterday –
   had very hard shells."

Page 15

Life sentence

COHUT PIGNTY is an anagram for TOUCH TYPING.

Page 20

Steps

Who was the first man to walk on the moon?
Who was the first strong man to walk on the moon?
Who was the first strong charming man on the moon?
Who was the first strong charming man to phone Illinois on the moon?
Strong charming man phone Illinois on the moon.
Strong charming man phone Illinois.
Phone Illinois strong charming man.
Phone Illinois charming strong man.
Phone Illinois charm strong man.

The answer is: Neil Armstrong.

Opposites

CURRIED CHICKEN
CRE CHICKEN
CRE ICE
CREAM ICE
ICE CREAM

Page 21

Whodunnit?

Major Hogg did it. The story should read as follows:

It was a dark and stormy night. Four people were sitting playing cards in Major Hogg's study.

Suddenly, the lights went out and somebody screamed. When they went on again, Mrs Pimple was lying on the floor, clutching her throat.

"My diamonds!" she cried, "They've stolen my diamonds!"

"Nobody move!" shouted Inspector Blair, as he ran through the open French windows.

In the snow outside was a set of footprints coming from a holly tree at the end of the lawn to the French windows. They seemed to go back up the garden, but stopped there.

"A very clever trick!" said Inspector Blair to himself. He strode into the study and looked carefully at everyone's shoes.

"What a crafty villain to have got away!" grunted Major Hogg.

"Not crafty enough!" said Inspector Blair, looking at the Major's snow-covered shoes. In one quick move he snapped a pair of handcuffs round the Major's wrists, and plucked a shining necklace from his pocket.

Page 25

Name the robot

The robot's name is FIL.

Page 26

Which animal?

A cat. The animal's face should look like this:

```
      X                                   X
     XXX                                 XXX
   XXXXX                                 XXXXX
  XXXXXXX                               XXXXXXX
 XXXXXXXX                               XXXXXXXX
 XXXXX                  XXXXX              XXXXX
 XX                                          XX



          XXXX                   XXXX
         XXXXX                   XXXXX
          XXX                     XXX


               X       X
              XX  XX
                  X
                  X
         X       X   X       X
          XXXX        XXXX

                 XXX
```

Page 32

Stop press

The gangster's face should look like this:

```
          XXXXXXXXXXXXX
         XXXXXXXXXXXXXXXXX
        XXXXXXXXXXXXXXXXXXXX
      XXX XXXXXXXXXXXXX    XXX
      XX      XXXXXXXXX      XXX
     XXX        XXX         XXX
     XX    XXXXX      XXXXX    XX
     X  XXXXXXXXX XXXXXXXXX   X
      XXXXXXX XXXXXXXXX XXXXXXX
      XXX XXXXXXXXXXXXXXXXXX XXX
    XXXX   XXXXXXX    XXXXXXX   XXXX
   X   XX                    XX  X
   X   XX                    XX  X
    X              X     X        X
     XX            X     X       XX
                  XXXXX          X
         X    XXXXXX XXXXXX      X
              XXX XXX            X
     X
      X                      X
       X               X
          X   X   X
```

Checkmate

In the picture on your screen, white won.

```
    XXXXX      XXXXX       XXXXX      XXXXX
    XXXXX      XXXXX       XXXXX      XXXXX
    XXXXX      XXXXX       XXXXX      XXXXX
XXXXX      XXXXX       XXXXX      XXXXX
XXXXX      XXXXX       XXXXX      XXXXX
XXXXX      XXXXX       XXXXX      XXXXX
    XXXXX      XXXXX       XXXXX      XXXXX
    XXXXX      XXXXX       XXXXX      XXXXX
    XXXXX      XXXXX       XXXXX      XXXXX
XXXXX      XXXXX       XXXXX      XXXXX
XXXXX      XXXXX     X WKNX        XXXXX
XXXXX      XXXXX       XXXXX      XXXXX
    XXXXX      XXXXX       XXXXX      XXXXX
    XXXXX      XXXXX       XXXXX      XXXXX
    XXXXX      XXXXX       XXXXX      XXXXX
XXXXX      XXXXX       XXXXX      XXXXX
XXXXX      XXXXX       XXXXX  WQ  XXXXX
XXXXX      XXXXX       XXXXX      XXXXX
    XXXXX      XXXXX       XXXXX      XXXXX
  X BQ X      XXXXX       XXXXX BK  XXXXX
    XXXXX      XXXXX       XXXXX      XXXXX
XXXXX      XXXXX       XXXXX      XXXXX
XXXXX      XXXXX  WK  XXXXX       XXXXX  WR
XXXXX      XXXXX       XXXXX      XXXXX
```

The rules of chess

Chess is a game played by two people, using a chequered board. Each side starts with sixteen pieces which can be moved across the chessboard in different ways. If one of your opponent's pieces is in the path of one of your pieces, you can take it.

The object of the game is to trap your opponent's "King" piece into a position where it is being threatened by one of your pieces, but it cannot move without being taken. This is called "checkmate" and means you have won.

Each side starts with the following pieces:

8 Pawns. You move these forwards, one square at a time. They can only take pieces that are one square diagonally in front of them.

2 Rooks, or Castles. These can be moved either sideways or up and down the board as many squares as you like.

2 Bishops. You move Bishops to follow the diagonal lines of squares on the board.

2 Knights. You move Knights two spaces in any direction and one square sideways, in an "L" shape.

1 Queen. This can be moved either up and down the board, or diagonally.

1 King. These can only be moved one square at a time, in any direction.

Glossary

Access time. The time it takes to obtain information from a storage device such as a **disk drive**.

Carriage return. Key or lever which, when pressed, makes the next letter you type appear at the left-hand **margin** and one line down from the previous letter.

Cat. Moveable spherical shape built into a **keyboard** which can be rolled by the palm of the hand to move the **cursor** round the screen.

Characters per second (CPS). A measure of printing speed for **printers**.

Command screen. Type of screen display which you see when you are giving instructions to the **word processor**.

Control key. Key which, when pressed with other keys, forms specific commands to the **word processor**.

CP/M. Stands for control program/microprocessor. A type of **operating system** commonly used in business microcomputers.

Cursor. Symbol on the screen which shows where the next character you type will appear.

Cursor control keys. Set of four keys, usually with arrows on, which move the **cursor** in four different directions when pressed.

Daisy wheel printer. Type of **printer** which produces high quality print from letter shapes moulded on to a circular print head.

Data. Computer information.

Dedicated word processor. Computer which is designed to be used only as a **word processor**.

Decimal tabs. Used to line up columns of figures so that the decimal points are directly underneath one another.

Delete. Rub out or erase.

Disk. Flat, circular piece of magnetically-coated plastic on which information can be stored using a **disk drive**.

Disk operating system (DOS). A program which tells the computer how to use a **disk drive**.

Dot matrix printer. Printer which forms letter shapes out of dots.

Double-density disk. Disk which can store twice the amount of information on one side as a single-density disk.

Double-sided disk. Disk which can store information on both sides.

Electronic mail. Communication between computers or **word processors** via telecommunications networks e.g. telephone, satellite.

Embedded commands. System of giving a **word processor formatting** instructions by typing them into the body of the text. Commands are usually preceded and followed by a special code. The word processor follows formatting instructions as text is printed out.

Escape key. Key which has a special function. It may enable you to switch between **command** and document screens, for example.

File. Document or section of your typing which you save, work on or print out separately from others.

Filename. Name consisting of letters and/or numbers which you give a **file** so the computer can identify the file once it has been saved.

Format. To lay out or arrange material on the screen or on paper.

Format line. Line at top of screen containing instructions such as position of **margins**, whether text is to be **justified** and so on. Used with systems which have **on-screen formatting**.

Function keys. Keys on the **keyboard** which have specific jobs.

Guide keys. Set of eight keys on a **keyboard** to which your fingers return after pressing different keys when **touch typing**.

Hard copy. A printout on paper.

Hardware. Parts of a computer, **word processor** or other electronic equipment.

Inserting. Adding letters or words between letters or words already on the screen.

Interface. Circuitry which allows a computer and another piece of **hardware** to communicate and work together.

Justification. Lining up of a column of text on both left and right-hand sides.

Keyboard. Part of the computer or **word processor** on which you type.

Kilobyte (K). Unit of measurement of computer **memory**.

Load. Transfer information stored on **disk** or tape to the **word processor**.

Mailmerge. Insert new, typed information into standard letters stored on **disk**.

Margin. Distance between edge of screen or paper and left-hand side of text.

Markers. Symbols you can use to identify the beginning and end of a section of text which you want to move, copy, **delete**, store or print out separately from the rest.

Memory. Part of the computer or **word processor** which stores programs or information you type in.

Menu. List of choices on the screen.

Microprocessor. Chip containing the control centre of a microcomputer or **word processor**.

Monitor. Screen specially designed for use with a computer or **word processor**.

Mouse. Wheeled device connected to a computer which can be rolled around on a flat surface. Its position is translated to a relative position on the screen; for instance, to make a choice from a **menu**.

On-screen formatting. System of giving a **word processor formatting** instructions. Text appears on the screen in the shape in which it will be printed out.

Operating system. Program containing instructions telling the computer how to work. It is either built in, or it needs to be **loaded** from **disk** before the computer can do anything.

Overwriting. Typing new words over words already on the screen in order to replace them.

Paging. Automatic numbering of sheets of paper done by **word processor**.

Passwords. Different codes for people sharing the same word processing system. When someone starts work on the **word processor**, they type in their password. The central computer then stores their text separately from other people's.

Peripheral. Any piece of equipment you connect to a computer, such as a **printer** or **disk drive**.

Pin feed. Method of pulling paper through a **printer** using little pins.

Pitch. Number of letters per inch (2.5cm) printed out by a **printer**. You can adjust the pitch on some printers.

Printer. Machine which prints text from a **word processor** or computer out on to paper.

Program. Set of instructions for a computer.

Proportional spacing. Ability of a **printer** to adjust space between letters according to their shape, to give a neater appearance.

QWERTY. Most common type of **keyboard**, named after the first six letters on the top row of letter keys.

Save. Store information on **disk** or tape.

Scrolling. Movement of a screen full of text either up, down, left or right.

Search and replace. Method of exchanging one word for another all through the text.

Shared resource system. Word processing system which consists of a number of **terminals** sharing central storage and printing facilities.

Shift key. Key which you press along with a letter key to make a typewriter or computer print a capital letter. With number or symbol keys, it prints the top symbol on the key.

Software. Computer programs and the instructions for how to use them.

Split screen. Screen display where one part is reserved for your instructions, another part for your typing etc.

Stand-alone system. Word processor which has its own storage and printing equipment.

Tab. A point, set in from the main left-hand **margin** by a specified amount, where lines can be started on the screen. Used for columns, starting paragraphs and so on.

Terminal. Keyboard and screen unit which shares equipment, such as storage or printing devices, with other terminals.

Thermal printer. Printer which forms letters out of dots using tiny sparks on heat-sensitive paper.

Touch typing. Typing without looking at your hands on the keys.

Tractor feed. Same as **pin feed**.

Word processor. Computer with a **program** which lets you type in, edit and store text.

Word wrap. Same as **wraparound**.

Working disk. Disk on which you are going to store **files** you are currently working on.

Wraparound. Automatic movement of **cursor** to next line down on screen display when previous line is full of characters.

Index